Cornwall's Industrial Past

Russell Holt

Tor Mark • Redruth

The Tor Mark series

Acknowledgements

The monochrome photographs are reproduced by kind permission of the Royal Institution of Cornwall, including that on the cover. The colour photographs are by the author except the following which are by Paul White: pages 1, 6b, 13b, 14a, 16, 17a, 18, 20a & b, 22, 23a & b, 24, 27b, 29a & b, 30b and 31a and cover (view at Chapel Porth, St Agnes).

First published 2003 by Tor Mark, PO Box 4, Redruth, Cornwall TR16 5YX
ISBN 0-85025-399-3
Printed in Great Britain by Cornwall Litho Ltd, Redruth

Introduction

It may come as a surprise to many holiday-makers, but from the mid-18th century Cornwall was as industrialised as the Midlands and North of England. It became one of the most important metal-mining areas in the world, produced a number of engineering 'firsts', exported machinery from local foundries to North America, South Africa and Australia, and reached its industrial peak in the mid-19th century. There are few counties in the UK with such a huge variety of industrial remains.

Cornwall is remote from the rest of the country and this, plus perhaps a greater dedication to conservation by local people and organisations, has meant many important industrial remains have survived, often in spectacular settings, and can now be visited. This book is an introduction to some of the most instructive sites.

For reasons of space, railway and tramway sites are only briefly touched on, as are fishing, farming and their related industries.

Natural power sources

Before the Industrial Revolution animal and wind power were important energy sources. Horse whim houses, where horses walked round and round turning a capstan, can be found in Cornwall but rarely contain machinery.

A horse whim house at Park Bottom, Pool (June 1978)

Left: The remains of a windmill on Predennack Downs, Lizard, SW693152 (October 1971)

Right: Tregargus Mill, near St Stephen, taken in April 1974. It was built in 1896 for crushing china-stone. The wheel is 10.75 m (35 ft) in diameter and overshot in type. It was restored in 1969 by the Cornish Water Wheels Preservation Society, now part of the Trevithick Society. The grinding pans are in the buildings on either side of the wheel

Windmills existed as well. Over seventy sites have been established in the county but only about six can still be seen. They were normally used for grain milling but occasionally to drain mines or quarries.

Although water power had also been in use for hundreds of years, after 1750 it took on a much more active role. In the UK as a whole, it is widely associated with grain and saw-milling, but in Cornwall it was also used in mining, gunpowder and china-stone grinding, as well as other industries.

There are three main types of waterwheel: breast-shot, where the water from the leat hits the wheel half-way up; undershot, which is like a paddle-wheel; and overshot, which is the most common in Cornwall.

Tregonning Mill, Stithians, a former grain mill with a breast-shot wheel (May 1976)

Hingham Mill, Egloshayle near Wadebridge, originally a grain mill, with an undershot paddle wheel of 6 metres diameter

Pennance Mill, Maenporth, Falmouth, a typical overshot wheel (September 2000)

Then and now, Botallack Mine near St Just around 1865, and in June 2002

Children are at work alongside women (known as 'bal-maidens') and older men in the 1860s. Many engine houses and stacks have survived, but most mine buildings were like these, built hastily and cheaply for short term use

Tin and copper mining

Tin and copper have been worked in Cornwall since prehistoric times – at first in streams and valley gravels, which continued into the medieval period on Bodmin Moor (SX180823) and the Land's End peninsula. With the increasing demand for both metals in the early 18th century, to make brass and bronze machine parts, the shallow mines could not produce enough ore. Pumps worked by water-wheels had limited capacity. The needs of the industry led to the invention and then rapid improvement of steam power by engineers such as Newcomen, Watt and Trevithick.

By the mid-19th century the Cornish beam engine reached its peak efficiency for pumping water, winding, and crushing ores. In 1856 copper production reached its maximum, 164,000 tons, and tin in 1871 reached 16,760 tons. There were hundreds of mines, though only a few were highly profitable: in consequence there are many abandoned mines to explore today.

East Pool 'whim' or winding engine as it looked in January 1976, now part of the Cornish Mines and Engines Centre at Pool

An ideal place to start studying Cornish mining is the Cornish Mines and Engines Centre (Industrial Discovery Centre) in Pool near Redruth (SW 673415) which is operated by The National Trust and the Trevithick Trust on two sites a few hundred metres apart. It includes audio-visual presentations, a static pumping engine and a working winding engine.

The Cornish Mines and Engines Centre at Pool, 2002

The Mineral Tramways Discovery Centre at Old Cowlin's Mill

Close by is the Mineral Tramways Discovery Centre (SW 670 408) at Old Cowlin's Mill. Situated in the heart of the mining country, the centre provides information on the footpath network which follows old tramways, railways and the adjacent mines around Carn Brea hill.

Mines worth a visit include Dolcoath (SW 662 405), the Bassett Mines between Piece and Carnkie (SW 681 394), Tincroft (SW 669 407) and South Crofty (SW 667 413).

The 'stamps' of West Basset Mines, at Carnkie near Redruth. Stamps were reciprocating hammers which pounded tin ore into gravel

Dolcoath Mine, the most productive and profitable of any mine in Cornwall's history, as it was in April 1999 (above) and in the nineteenth century (below)

King Edward Mine at Troon, near Camborne, 1999

Whilst in the Redruth area, a visit should be made to the King Edward Mine near Troon (SW 664388) where the many aspects of 'tin dressing' (processing) can be seen.

King Edward Mine was originally South Condurrow Mine, which started work in 1848. When underground production ended, it was taken over for student use by Camborne School of Mines and re-named King Edward Mine. It is now an excellent museum.

The photograph shows a shaking table, which uses a vibrating motion to separate out the tin concentrate as it passes over the surface in a continuous stream of water

At St Agnes is the Blue Hills Tin Streams Centre (SW727517) where small amounts of tin metal are produced. The photograph above is a general photograph of the site in 2002, whilst the lower photograph shows the valley in the 1890s

Right: The stamps at the Blue Hills Tin Streams Centre

Below: Stamps in action at Tolgus Tin

Tolgus Tin near Redruth, full of working tin processing machinery

One of the last tin streaming works in Cornwall is Tolgus Tin, near Redruth (SW 690443), where waterwheels, tin stamps and processing equipment have recently been restored.

Poldark Mine at Wendron near Helston (SW 682316) has underground tours and the old Greensplat china clay beam engine is part of the surface display.

Right: This beam engine came from the Greensplat china clay works, St Austell, and is now part of the display at Poldark Mine Museum (1984)

Below: The Greensplat engine house, as it was about 1950

Geevor Mine, now a museum (June 2002)

In the Land's End area, Geevor Mine Museum stands above the Atlantic cliffs north of St Just (SW 375345). The mine closed in 1990 but Cornwall County Council and Pendeen Community Heritage now operate it.

Close by is Levant Mine (SW 368345) which started as a copper mine about 1820 but began to produce tin after 1852. In 1919 the man-engine (a lifting device) collapsed, killing 31 miners and injuring many more. Eventually the mine closed in 1930: it had worked to a depth of 640 m and over 1.5 km out under the sea. The beam engine was saved in 1935 by the Cornish Engines Preservation Society, probably the first industrial archaeologists in the UK. During the 1990s the Trevithick Society restored the engine and it now works regularly under steam.

Opposite, top: Levant Mine in 2002. The whim or winding engine is on the left and the pumping engine on the right. The site is owned by The National Trust and operated by the Trevithick Society

Opposite, below: The Levant 'dry' in 1894 – a changing room where miners left their underground clothing – considered very advanced when it was built in 1889 at a cost of £1000

The Crowns engine houses, June 1998

One kilometre west of Levant above the cliffs is Botallack Mine (SW 364332). The two engine houses situated just above sea-level are known as the Crowns section of the mine, which extended out under the sea in the Diagonal Shaft to 414 m. In 1865 the Duke and Duchess of Cornwall (later King Edward VII and Queen Alexandra) visited the mine and toured underground. By the late 19th century most work had finished, but in 1907-14 it was reworked for arsenic, thus leaving some of the best arsenic processing ovens and flues in the county. The Count House (office) is now a visitor centre run by The National Trust.

Opposite, top left: The Diagonal Shaft, in 1865

Opposite, top right: The Botallack arsenic processing works, February 2002. Arsenic production became a significant business for Cornish mines in the late Victorian period, when many spoil heaps were worked over again to extract it. Copper arsenite was used as a green pigment in wallpaper and fabrics, including those of William Morris, and had unintentional poisonous effects. Arsenic products were used for fly-papers and weedkillers, and also for medical purposes – not least by Dr Crippen

Opposite, below: The dressing floors and calciner stack being built in 1907

Above: The Prince of Wales Shaft of Phoenix United Mine near Minions on Bodmin Moor, where much restoration has taken place in recent years and a group of other buildings surrounds the engine house

Left: There is a small Heritage Centre housed in this engine house at Minions

South Caradon Mine near Minions, best approached from Tokenbury Corner

At the other end of the county, 7 km north of Liskeard in east Cornwall, stands Caradon Hill. The granite mass is encircled by several important mines including South Caradon (SX 269 698) which has so far been relatively untouched by conservation and Phoenix United which has – especially around the Prince of Wales shaft (SX 266 721). The village of Minions has a small heritage centre (SX 261 714) which has information on the industrial history of the area and its prehistoric remains, notably the Hurlers stone circles which are side by side with the mining remains.

The Wheal Martyn China Clay Museum at Carthew near St Austell has a viewing gallery where you can observe this working clay pit. The museum itself preserves many historic systems and equipment – see opposite

China clay

China clay (decomposed granite) extraction is a recent newcomer to the industrial landscape of Cornwall. It was discovered by William Cookworthy about 1746, west of Helston, and shortly afterward around St Stephen in mid-Cornwall. As tin and copper declined in the late 19th century, china clay production expanded rapidly. As pits became larger and deeper many of the old industrial buildings disappeared.

However, one very important site remains, Wheal Martyn China Clay Museum (SX 005 554) 4km north of St Austell on B3274. A visit to Wheal Martyn is essential to understand the clay industry. There are working waterwheels, mica drags, settling tanks and dries. As a follow-up, a walk through the Luxulyan valley (SX 058 572) would prove interesting: the 1840 Treffry railway viaduct is also an aqueduct and there are remains of wheel pits, leats, clay processing and railway inclines.

A water wheel once used for pumping clay slurry (above) and a series of 'drags' (below). Those on the left separated out sand, those in the middle caught mica, and the clay slurry passed through to the settling pits on the right

The Cheesewring Quarry, August 2002 (SX258724), a large granite quarry near Minions on the edge of Bodmin Moor. The Liskeard & Caradon Railway was built in 1846 to Moorswater, where granite and metal ores were transferred to the Liskeard & Looe Union Canal. In 1860 the railway was extended all the way to Looe

Quarrying

The geology of Cornwall has provided a wide range of useful building materials, especially slate, serpentine and granite. Stone has been used for building since prehistoric times, from the giant megaliths of the Land's End peninsula to castles such as Pendennis in Falmouth and the lighthouses around the coast.

Above right: At Poltesco (SW727156) near Cadgwith there is an old serpentine factory of 1866. Serpentine was very popular in Victorian times as a substitute for marble, and serpentine ornaments were made fashionable by Prince Albert

Below right: Another major area of granite quarrying lies just inland from Penryn, centred on Mabe. This photograph of Penryn in the early 1900s shows piles of granite on the edge of the quay (behind the lamp-post for example) waiting to be loaded onto a coaster

THE QUAY, PENRYN. 25

A walk along the cliffs between Trebarwith Strand (SX 047 865) and Tintagel (SX 055 886) follows a line of old slate workings.

Delabole Slate Quarry in north Cornwall (shown opposite) has a visitor centre. Slate was first quarried here in the 13th century and the pit is now over 150 m deep.

Last but not least, the Carnglaze Slate Caverns (SX 187 668), 7 km west of Liskeard, contain underground workings on a scale similar to those in north Wales.

Right: This winch at Tintagel is a reminder of the days when slate from Delabole Quarry (opposite) and from the cliff slate quarries (top) was loaded into small boats which beached on the sand in Tintagel cove

The Carbis brick and tile works near Roche (SX002596) as it was in June 1982

Other industries

Some industries, like foundries, smelters and the manufacture of explosives, relate to mining and quarrying. Lime burning has a strong tradition around the coast due to the acid soils. Bricks and tiles were produced throughout the county, but especially around Calstock in the Tamar valley and the St Austell area.

Communications

All these heavy industries required transport links, and river and sea transport were vital. There are numerous former river quays and small ports all around the county, as well as the large port of Falmouth with its dry docks. Cotehele Quay was one of many on the Tamar, and its grain mill, saw-pit, lime-kilns and warehouses have been preserved. Looe exported granite from Caradon, whilst Boscastle shipped grain, slate and manganese ore.

Cornwall had little connection with the canal era in the late 18th century, and only the Bude Canal has left significant remains.

Bude Canal Basin as it appeared in 1984. The sea locks are at the back left. There is a small museum on the right of the picture

Above: Cotehele Quay near Calstock. There are lime-kilns to the right of the pub, and more out of shot to the left. The quay is also home to the Tamar sailing barge Shamrock *(below)*

Very individual milestones can still be found, such as these at Stithians (left) and south of Kit Hill, where an old road led through Luckett to Horsebridge

Ancient trackways can still be traced in the Land's End area leading down to Penzance and St Ives. These would have been used by traders in the Bronze and Iron Ages. With the development of mining in the Middle Ages, a system of tracks began to develop, along which trains of packhorses carried the produce of the mines down to the ports.

It was not until the turnpike trusts were established in Cornwall between 1754 and 1863 – the period of the mining boom – that roads at all suitable for wheeled transport were created.

Cornwall played a significant part in the development of railways. Initially these were horse-drawn tramroads linking mines to ports, such as the Poldice-Portreath tramway. The great Cornish engineer Trevithick built steam locomotives in the early 1800s but these never achieved a practical application. In 1834 steam locomotives were introduced into the county on the Bodmin & Wadebridge railway. Some of the lines in the Redruth area now form part of the Mineral Tramways Project, and those around Caradon Hill pass granite quarries and mines.

Above: This magnificent railway viaduct at Luxulyan (SX 055572) was built in the 1840s as part of a horse-drawn railway which was intended to run from Par to Newquay

Right: The Portreath incline plane (SW 657450) seen in 1972 when it was less overgrown and built-up than it now is. A stationary steam engine lowered the wagons down the incline to the harbour, which is to the right of the photograph

Museums

A number of museums around the county have information on past industries, including:

Blue Hills Tin Streams Centre (01872) 553341
Camborne School of Mines in Pool (01209) 714866
Cornish Mines and Engines Centre, Pool (01209) 216657
Delabole Slate Quarry (01840) 212242
Geevor Tin Mine, Pendeen (01736) 788662
Levant Steam Engine (01736) 786156
National Maritime Museum in Falmouth (01326) 313388
Mineral Tramways Discovery Centre, Pool (01209) 612917
Poldark Mine, Wendron (01326) 563166
Royal Cornwall Museum in Truro (01872) 272205,
Tolgus Tin, Portreath (01209) 215185
Wheal Martyn Museum (01726) 850362

and local museums in:

Helston (01326) 564027   St Agnes (01872) 552181
Redruth (01209) 216760   Bude (01288) 353576

Some useful books if you want to explore the subject further

Charlestown Richard and Bridget Larn (Tor Mark)

China clay – traditional methods in Cornwall Charles Thurlow (Tor Mark)

China clay from Devon and Cornwall: the modern china clay industry Charles Thurlow (Cornish Hillside)

Cornish engine houses D B Barton (Tor Mark)

Cornish inventors Carolyn Martin (Tor Mark)

The Cornish mining industry J A Buckley (Tor Mark)

Cornish mining – underground J A Buckley (Tor Mark)

Cornwall's mining heritage Peter Stanier (Twelveheads)

Cornwall's railways Tony Fairclough (Tor Mark)

Exploring Cornish mines, 5 vols, Kenneth Brown and Bob Acton (Landfall)

Lost ports of Cornwall (Tor Mark)

Mining in Cornwall, 5 vols, L J Bullen (Tempus)